RICHARD SIMMONS
COOKIN' ON BROADWAY

P9-CMX-878

WHERE'S THE FLAVOR? Well, you finally wore me down! You finally forced my hand! The cat is out of the bag! Below is a list of my SUPER "SAVING" SECRETS - these are some of my tried and true, time-tested tips as to how to keep the calorie count and fat content down in your food without sacrificing the flavor! I've included spices, dips, dressings and alternative foods so that you have the option of making your meal even MORE healthy for you. As the Church Lady would say, "Now, isn't that special"?

"I Can't Believe It's Not Butter"
I think this tastes EXACTLY like butter. And, you can have one TABLESPOON of this as opposed to one TEA-SPOON of regular butter!

Low Fat Mayonnaise
This tastes better to me than fat-free mayonnaise (but, you can be your own judge) – try it in all your favorites – tuna-fish salad, egg-salad, pasta salad…

Extracts
What the heck am I talking about? You know, vanilla, almond, coconut, lemon and orange extract – just to name a few. Extracts come in many flavors and add a uniqueness (like "moi") to food WITHOUT added calories!

"Pam" Cooking Spray
One of my favorites! It's a way to add flavor and a smidgen of fat to cooking with virtually ZERO calories. I like to use "Pam" (as my oil) and a little bit of vinegar on my salads as a dressing.

Roasted Garlic
Mmmm! Mmmm! Mama Mia! Trust me – once you start making your own roasted garlic – you'll be spreading it on everything from Italian bread to breakfast waffles (okay, maybe not waffles…) Look on page 28 for my tip on roasting garlic.

Salad Dressing
Most times I use the REAL DEAL like "Wishbone Italian" – it's fabulous. My motto is: "Everything in moderation". If you don't feel like using a fat-free or low-fat salad dressing, please, please, please check the serving size on the back of the bottle. Remember, those crispy leaves of lettuce and juicy tomatoes are for eating NOT drowning!

"EggBeaters"
These days, we're all watching cholesterol and fat intake (even you young whipper-snappers!). "EggBeaters" are fantastic in an omelet, scrambled, poached or fried. And, they save me from eating all the extra fat in the yolks of real eggs.

"Worcestershire Sauce"
Yes, it might be a distant county in England but, it also adds a powerful and tasty flavoring to food. Heard of A-1? Well, I use Worcestershire as my own "special sauce" on steak.

Tobasco Sauce
Holy Smokes! is right! Yes, you might feel a tiny "bite back" from this tangy sauce but, growing up in Louisiana, we practically LIVED on this stuff! I've tried it on everything from crawfish to scrambled eggs. You should too!

Low Fat Buttermilk
Creamy, buttery, and low in calories – who could ask for anything more?

Low Fat Cottage Cheese
Trust me, you'll never miss the fat that's missing from low-fat cottage cheese. Plus, it's a great protein and calcium source. Milk isn't the only thing that "does a body good"!

Shallots

I call these little things "Onions Plus". You may or may not have heard of them, but they are a definite MUST TRY. A great compliment to salads, sandwiches, and all sorts of side dishes.

Low Sodium Chicken Stock

Honestly adds flavor to many recipes when water just won't cut it. And, who needs the extra salt from regular chicken stock? Certainly not this spring chicken!

Fat Free Sour Cream

I can't even tell fat-free sour cream from the real thing! I love it on my nachos and baked potatoes – which, proves my theory that *Coca-Cola* isn't the only "Real Thing".

Lime and Lemon

Fish. Rice. Vegetables. And, yes, even Key lime pie. Lemon and lime are among my favorite fruits that provide a low-cal, juicy dressing for many of my favorite dishes.

Herbs and Spices

There's nothing like fresh herbs and spices - not only do they smell delectable, but they also add flavor "pizazz" to every meal. Try using some fresh herbs and spices instead of overloading on the salt. And, remember, try not to keep spices more than 6 months - they lose their flavor after that.

GETTING TO KNOW YOUR KITCHEN

Getting to know your kitchen – getting to know all about – your kitchen. Well, I may be no Yul Brenner, but I certainly am King of my kitchen.

Kitchen Things

Here are a few of my favorite kitchen things to help keep my meals stay healthy, fresh, satisfying and in appropriate portions.:
* Teflon saute pan
* Steamer
* Measuring cups (8 oz. And 4 cp. Sizes - for both dry and liquid ingredients)
* Measuring spoons (all sizes)
* Blender
* Food Processor
* Good, sharp knives
* Clean cutting boards, spoons, strainers
* Different size pots with covers
* Different size bowls
* Meat Thermometer
* Food Scale
* *Tupperware/ Pampered Chef* Storage

Measure it Up

I know, I know - I don't want to be "Auntie Mame"-ish here and drive you batty - but, I must repeat myself in saying that proper measuring is a key ingredient to successful cooking. It's the only way to be sure that you're getting EXACTLY what you "think" you're getting. Did you know that using as little as one teaspoon of oil MORE than you actually use can add up to as much as a 5 lb. weight gain over a year? Who needs that? Certainly not these tender thighs! Knowing some measuring basics will make it easier for you to be as accurate as possible and keep those pounds OFF!
* Tablespoon - 16 tablespoons in 1 cup
* Teaspoon - 3 teaspoons in 1 tablespoon
* Cup - 8 oz. in 1 cup
* Pound - 16 ounces in 1 lb.

P.S. ALWAYS level out dry ingredients when measuring

What to do if it's not a whole window? Many times when cooking you use just a little of this or that and when divided out for the number of portions it's no where near a whole food mover window. What to do? As I did for this cookbook I chose the window that best represents it and used extras to pick up half windows. So, don't worry – Just enjoy!

GUENEVIERE'S UPSIDE DOWN FRITTATA
BY CAROL HELMLINGER

"I lost 24 lbs in three months on the FoodMover program. I am more aware of the amount and types of foods that I'm eating. I love the vitamins, I take them every morning. I try to get in my exercise 5x a week. I'm not going to give up."

"The FoodMover is easy. I have better eating habits and finally I'm seeing results on weight-loss."

TATARS FOR THE STARS
BY CHRISTINE MARCANTONIO

ALL THAT WRAP

BY JOANNE PRASOLY

INGREDIENTS

- 6 oz Egg Beaters or egg whites
- 1/4 cup mushrooms
- 1/4 cup chopped onions
- 1 oz low fat cheddar cheese shredded
- 1 6" flour tortilla
- 1 tbsp chopped parsley
- cooking spray

DIRECTIONS [1 SERVINGS]

1. Heat tortilla until warm.
2. Spray and heat a skillet.
3. Sauté onions until brown, add mushrooms, and heat until mushrooms are soft.
4. Add egg whites or Egg Beaters and cook through and then add shredded cheddar and fold in parsley.
5. Roll in soft tortilla and serve.
6. Optional garnish with salsa.

Tip: Serve with Salsa. There are many different types of flour tortillas available in your supermarket, even flavored kinds. Most flour tortillas are nutritionally the same; compare the labels and then chose your favorite flavor.

FOODMOVER WINDOWS TO CLOSE PER SERVING

NUTRITION INFORMATION PER SERVING	
CALORIES	287
PROTEIN	31g
CARBOHYDRATE	28g
TOTAL FAT	5.6g
SODIUM	528mg

BROADWAY BREAKFAST STRATA

BY DARLENE FOSTER

Tip: No this isn't named after Erik Estrada! Strata are usually considered Italian in origin, consisting of many layers. This is a great brunch dish. Look for packages of breakfast sausage that has less than 30 calories, and less than a gram of fat per sausage

INGREDIENTS

- 6 slices whole wheat toast
- 8 fl oz low fat buttermilk
- 8 oz low fat shredded cheddar cheese
- 1/2 cup sliced mushrooms
- 6 chopped green onions
- 1/2 green bell pepper
- 6.4 oz package low fat breakfast sausage (sliced thin)
- 2 cups Egg Beaters

Pam butter flavored cooking spray

DIRECTIONS | 8 SERVINGS

1. Preheat oven to 400°. Spray a square baking dish lightly with cooking spray.
2. Layer bread on the bottom of the baking dish. Sprinkle half the shredded cheese over the bread.
3. Spray a nonstick skillet with Pam. Add mushrooms, onions, bell pepper and sausage. Sauté vegetables until they begin to get tender and sausages are thoroughly cooked.
4. Spread vegetable/sausage mixture evenly in baking dish. Sprinkle the other half of the cheese over the vegetable layer. Pour Egg Beaters over contents of baking dish.
5. Place in oven and bake for approximately 40 minutes.
6. Remove from oven, cut into 8 equal servings, and serve hot.
7. Optional garnish with cherry tomatoes and parsley.

FOODMOVER WINDOWS TO CLOSE PER SERVING

NUTRITION INFORMATION PER SERVING	
CALORIES	190
PROTEIN	22.3g
CARBOHYDRATE	17.6g
TOTAL FAT	3.7g
SODIUM	692mg

GUENEVIERE'S UPSIDE DOWN FRITTATA

BY CAROL HELMLINGER

INGREDIENTS

3 egg whites
1/2 egg yolk
1/4 cup non-fat cottage cheese
2 tsp grated Parmesan cheese
1/2 cup sliced mushrooms
1 tsp italian seasoning
1 tsp chopped garlic
1/4 cup chopped bell pepper
1/4 cup chopped onion
1/4 cup chopped red pepper
pepper to taste
Non-fat cooking spray

DIRECTIONS | 1 SERVINGS |

1. Lightly coat the skillet with non-stick spray.
2. Sauté garlic, onions, chopped pepper until they start to soften, then add mushrooms, Italian seasoning and pepper.
3. Combine yolk, egg whites and cheese and pour into skillet with veggies and cook until eggs are firm.
4. Flip upside down and serve.

Tip: It's not upside down because she dropped it. A frittata is a firm thick Italian omelet that may contain a variety of chopped ingredients, including meat or vegetables.

FOODMOVER WINDOWS TO CLOSE PER SERVING

NUTRITION INFORMATION PER SERVING	
CALORIES	129
PROTEIN	19.7g
CARBOHYDRATE	3.3g
TOTAL FAT	3.6g
SODIUM	443mg

ANYTHING GOES FRENCH TOAST

BY LISA CHASE

Tip: Yes there are almonds in the recipe but we spread them out so the fat and flavor are dispersed throughout all those yummy bites. To get more of that concentrated flavor extracts are used; if you are not crazy about almond switch to any other extract. There are many flavors available in the bakery section of your supermarket.

INGREDIENTS

- 1/2 cup Egg Beaters
- 1/4 cup non fat milk
- 1/4 tsp almond extract
- 1/4 cup slivered almonds
- 3 tsp sugar
- 4 slices lite whole wheat bread
- Pam cooking spray

DIRECTIONS | 2 SERVINGS

1. Mix all ingredients together except bread.
2. Soak bread into mixture and cook in a heated Pam sprayed pan. Cook on one side for approximately 1 to 2 minutes and then flip and cook for an additional 1 minute.
3. Optional garnish with fresh oranges and strawberries (close a fruit window).

FOODMOVER WINDOWS TO CLOSE PER SERVING

NUTRITION INFORMATION PER SERVING	
CALORIES	219
PROTEIN	13.7g
CARBOHYDRATE	26g
TOTAL FAT	7.9g
SODIUM	287mg

TATARS FOR THE STARS

BY CHRIS MARCANTONIO

INGREDIENTS

- 2 cups fat-free hash brown potatoes (shreds or chunks)
- 4 oz of your favorite low fat cheese
- 1/2 cup diced lightly steamed carrots
- 1/2 cup (small pieces) lightly steamed broccoli crowns
- 1/3 cup chopped onion
- 1/2 cup sliced mushrooms
- 2 tbsp green onions (finely chopped)
- 1 cup liquid egg substitute
- 1/2 cup skim milk
- 1 tbsp horseradish
- 1 tsp salt (optional)
- pepper to taste
- dill to taste
- non-stick cooking spray

DIRECTIONS 4 (3/4) CUP SERVINGS

1. Preheat the oven to 425°.
2. Thaw hash browns and drain out excess water.
3. Spray the bottom of a 9-10" pie plate with non-stick spray.
4. Place the hashbrowns in the pie plate.
5. Spray the top with non-stick spray.
6. Bake the hash brown crust for 20 minutes.
7. While the crust is baking, sauté the carrots, broccoli, chopped onion and mushrooms in a skillet which has been sprayed with cooking spray until just tender.
8. Mix the egg substitute with the milk, salt, pepper, horseradish and green onion.
9. Remove the crust from the oven and add your cheeses, veggies, and egg mixture.
10. Reduce the oven temperature to 350° and continue to bake 20 minutes or until the center is done.
11. Let stand for approximately 10 minutes. Enjoy!!!

Tip: Note: Look for the frozen hash browns that do not have added fat. Hash browns come uncooked in the freezer section or you can make your own by shredding fresh potatoes. If using red potatoes keep skin on for extra color. This is a fabulous potato recipe; it may look difficult but do not worry, it's not and it's worth it! Shhh... The secret is in the horseradish.

FOODMOVER WINDOWS TO CLOSE PER SERVING

NUTRITION INFORMATION PER SERVING	
CALORIES	209
PROTEIN	18.9g
CARBOHYDRATE	39g
TOTAL FAT	2g
SODIUM	1148mg

SILVER SCREEN TUNA MELT
BY NANCY HARDEE

"I just started the program and I'm so excited. I've been looking for a convenient way to keep track of my calories and servings. Now thanks to the FoodMover I have my weight under control. The FoodMover fits my personality."

GIVE MY REGARDS TO BROCCOLI
BY TAMMY ROJAS

"I've been using the FoodMover program since spring of 1998 and have lost 175 lbs. I have been able to maintain my loss for over a year now. I love the new FoodMover cookbook; it takes the guess work out of cooking. My FoodMover has become my best friend. It never lets me down and it never lies to me. It is kind to me and allows me to enjoy life without feeling deprived."

A STREET CAR NAMED BRUSCHETTA

BY JUDY LENTEY

INGREDIENTS

- 1-1/4 cup chopped plum tomato (in its own juices)
- 1 tbsp chopped basil
- 1/4 cup chopped red onion
- 2 tsp chopped garlic
- 2 tsp olive oil
- 1 tsp chopped oregano
- 2 tsp lime juice
- 1/2 italian bread sliced on a slant into 12 - 1" pieces
- cooking spray
- black pepper to taste

DIRECTIONS 2 SERVINGS

1. Mix all ingredients except bread together and chill.
2. Spray Italian bread with cooking spray and lightly toast.
3. Top toast with tomato mixture and toast.

Tip: A quick, easy appetizer that I like to make at home. This bruschetta doesn't have to be on Italian bread; French bread works great too. In this recipe it's important to chop the garlic fine, fine, fine! Because large chunks of garlic do not make a Fine bruschetta!

FOODMOVER WINDOWS TO CLOSE PER SERVING

NUTRITION INFORMATION PER SERVING	
CALORIES	190
PROTEIN	4.5g
CARBOHYDRATE	23.6g
TOTAL FAT	8.8g
SODIUM	264mg

GIVE MY REGARDS TO BROCCOLI

BY TAMMY ROJAS

Special Tip:
If you are not a garlic lover, reduce the amount to 2 pieces. To steam broccoli put in a steamer in a saucepan over simmering water, and cover top, or you can do in a little water in a microwave safe bowl in the microwave until just tender.

Tip: I'm not closing any fat windows because the fat is included in the protein window (see food-mover window page)

INGREDIENTS

- 2 cooked and diced chicken breasts (4 oz each)
- 2 cups chopped fresh broccoli (steamed)
- 1 diced red bell pepper
- 1 diced yellow bell pepper
- 4 cloves fresh pressed garlic (not the bulb, just 4 pieces of it!)
- 1/2 cup low fat mayonnaise
- 2 tbsp chopped fresh dill
- 2 oz shredded low fat cheddar cheese
- 4 6 oz pita pockets, split
- 4 green lettuce leaves

DIRECTIONS 4 SERVINGS

1. Combine all ingredients in a large mixing bowl.
2. Divide into 4 equal servings.
3. Fill pita pockets with lettuce leaf and chicken mixture. Enjoy!

FOODMOVER WINDOWS TO CLOSE PER SERVING

NUTRITION INFORMATION PER SERVING	
CALORIES	482
PROTEIN	41.6g
CARBOHYDRATE	48g
TOTAL FAT	13.3g
SODIUM	763mg

A NIGHT ON BROADWAY BURGER

BY CHRISTINE MEYERS

INGREDIENTS

- 3 oz raw ground turkey
- 1/4 cup chopped mushrooms
- 1/4 cup shredded zucchini
- 1 tsp Egg Beaters
- 1 oz part skim milk mozzarella cheese
- 1/2 plain hamburger roll/bun or kaiser roll
- 1 slice onion
- 2 tsp Dijon mustard
- Pam non stick cooking spray
- pinch garlic
- pinch pepper
- pinch salt

DIRECTIONS [1 SERVINGS]

1. Mix in bowl turkey, mushroom, zucchini, and Egg Beaters, garlic powder, salt and pepper.
2. Make a patty; spray fry pan with cooking spray. Cook burger and flip to cook other side (about 5 minutes each side).
3. Finish burger in 350° oven.
4. Place cheese on burger and when finished place in bun which has been spread with mustard on the bottom.
5. Sauté onion in cooking spray and place on burger and serve.

Tip: Lower sodium content by not adding salt and mustard. This is a great way to get your kids to eat more vegetables. No need to close any fat windows; the fat is accounted for in the protein windows. If you don't like using Dijon mustard any mustard will do; honey mustard gives a nice taste. Garnish with fresh veggies.

FOODMOVER WINDOWS TO CLOSE PER SERVING

NUTRITION INFORMATION PER SERVING	
CALORIES	295
PROTEIN	27g
CARBOHYDRATE	16g
TOTAL FAT	13.8g
SODIUM	460mg

SILVER SCREEN TUNA MELT

BY NANCY HARDEE

Tip: Tip on toasting the bread (don't burn it). Why no extra fat windows? It's in the protein.

INGREDIENTS

- 1 slice toasted rye bread
- 1 tbsp low fat mayonnaise
- 2 oz white meat tuna in water (drained)
- 1 tbsp chopped red onion
- 1 tbsp chopped celery
- 1/4 cup chopped pineapple (in its own natural juices)
- 2 oz low fat shredded cheddar

DIRECTIONS | 1 SERVINGS

1. Toast bread.
2. Mix tuna with veggies and mayo.
3. Top bread with tuna mixture and top with chopped pineapple and grated cheese.
4. Place under broiler until the cheese is melted and bubbly.

FOODMOVER WINDOWS TO CLOSE PER SERVING

NUTRITION INFORMATION PER SERVING	
CALORIES	360
PROTEIN	29g
CARBOHYDRATE	35.6g
TOTAL FAT	12g
SODIUM	714mg

GODFATHER PASTA FAGIOLE
BY KIMBERLY AUFMAN

"The FoodMover has changed my life by making me aware of proper portion sizes. I am confident that in time the extra weight will come off! It's great and I don't even feel deprived."

DANCING CHUNKY GAZPACHO
BY PATRICIA MERKLE

"I needed energy and confidence, really needed it. I train and raise Arabian horses as friends and companions. Richard's FoodMover and exercise tapes have helped tremendously. Today I worked two horses, graded the ground for a garden and exercised to the Blast Off tape. Now I know I can make it. Thank you."

BLACK BIRDIES SOUP

BY RUTH MC CARTHY

Tip: Don't be afraid to make fresh beans. Soak beans overnight and discard water, cover beans 2x depth and boil lower and simmer till softened. Add water if needed while cooking, discard leftover water at end.

INGREDIENTS

2	15 oz cans black beans rinsed
1	cup chopped carrots
3	cups low sodium chicken stock
2	large onions chopped
2	celery stalks diced
1/2	cup chopped carrots
1/4	cup chopped parsley
6	garlic cloves
2	bay leaf
1	tsp salt
1	tsp pepper

cooking spray
fat free sour cream for garnish
optional carrot curl garnish

DIRECTIONS **4 SERVINGS**

1. Boil beans with chicken stock 5 minutes.
2. Lower heat and simmer 1 hour.
3. Meanwhile spray skillet with cooking spray and sauté garlic, onions, celery, carrots until soft.
4. Combine veggies with bean mixture, add bay leaf, parsley, salt and pepper and simmer 1 hour more until flavors combine.
5. Puree soup and serve.

FOODMOVER WINDOWS TO CLOSE PER SERVING

NUTRITION INFORMATION PER SERVING	
CALORIES	196
PROTEIN	12.5g
CARBOHYDRATE	35.2g
TOTAL FAT	1.4g
SODIUM	669mg

DANCING CHUNKY GAZPACHO!!!

BY PATRICIA MERKLE

INGREDIENTS

1 large can salt-free tomato juice (1 qt, 14 oz)
1/4 green pepper
1 cucumber
1/2 ripe tomato
1/2 carrot
1/4 onion
1 clove fresh garlic
4 celery sticks
sprig cilantro to taste
dash cumin
dash salt

DIRECTIONS 4 (2 CUP) SERVINGS

1. Chop the veggies until chunky.
2. Mix all ingredients together and chill in the refrigerator.
3. Measure out 2 cups over 1/2 cup ice.

Tip: This is a midsummer refresher that is filling. Optional garnish with additional celery sticks and a cilantro sprig.

Tip: Wondering about cumin? Cumin is a herb that grows in the Mediterranean with small white or rose colored flowers. It is also found in India, China and Mexico and is used for its fruits or seeds. Cumin has a distinctive aroma and taste.

FOODMOVER WINDOWS TO CLOSE PER SERVING

NUTRITION INFORMATION PER SERVING	
CALORIES	99
PROTEIN	4g
CARBOHYDRATE	24g
TOTAL FAT	0.5g
SODIUM	160mg

HAPPY FELLA PASTA FAGIOLE

BY KIMBERLY AUFMAN

Tip: Why don't you try freezing all those extra servings? I just know you have some of those "Tupperware" or "Pampered Chef" containers lying around! This is a great meal to eat repeatedly for that "New York" state of mind. PS... there are many things you can use instead of smoked turkey, although it may change the nutritionals, like low fat ham, smoked chicken breast.

INGREDIENTS

- 1   cup dry macaroni
- 1   29 oz can tomato sauce
- 2   15 oz cans great northern beans, drained
- 1   pound lean smoked turkey, cut into chunks
- 4   cups water
- 1   tbsp olive oil
- 1/2 cup water
- 1   tsp onion powder
- 2   tbsp minced garlic
- 1/2 cup chopped onion
- 1   cup chopped spinach (if frozen drain)
- 2   tbsp fresh chopped parsley
- 2   tbsp fresh chopped oregano
- 1/2 tsp black pepper
- 1/4 tsp red chili powder
- 2   tbsp grated Parmesan cheese

DIRECTIONS 13 (1 CUP) SERVINGS

1. In a large stockpot add olive oil and sauté garlic, and onions. Add all additional ingredients except the pasta and heat to boiling.
2. Reduce heat and simmer, covered for 10 minutes with 1/2 cup water.
3. Return to boil and add pasta, stirring occasionally for 15 minutes.
4. Add spinach at end; sprinkle with a small amount of Parmesan cheese and serve.

FOODMOVER WINDOWS TO CLOSE PER SERVING

NUTRITION INFORMATION PER SERVING	
CALORIES	172
PROTEIN	13.4g
CARBOHYDRATE	26.6g
TOTAL FAT	1.8g
SODIUM	840mg

THE SOUP MUST GO ON

BY BOB GRAVES

INGREDIENTS

- 2 large portabella mushrooms cut into chunks
- 4 carrots sliced
- 20 green beans cut into pieces
- 2 stalks celery sliced
- 1/2 medium onion chopped
- 1 10 oz bag fresh spinach cleaned and chopped small
- 1 clove minced garlic
- 2 fresh tomatoes or 1 can tomatoes with juice
- 2 cans low sodium vegetable broth and 2 cans of water
- 1/3 small can (4 oz) tomato paste
- 2 bay leaves
- 1 tbsp olive oil
- black pepper to taste

DIRECTIONS 4 SERVINGS

1. Sauté: garlic, onions, carrots and celery in olive oil until soft.
2. Add remaining ingredients except spinach.
3. Bring ingredients to boil and simmer for 30 minutes.
4. Add spinach and simmer for another 5-10 minutes.

Tip: Save some spinach for garnish; make sure to chop spinach small.

FOODMOVER WINDOWS TO CLOSE PER SERVING

NUTRITION INFORMATION PER SERVING	
CALORIES	124
PROTEIN	4.6g
CARBOHYDRATE	17g
TOTAL FAT	5.2g
SODIUM	108mg

TEPETANGO TANGO SOUP

BY TERESA REVELES

Tip: What is a daikon radish? It's a big spicy long white radish tasting vegetable. For the same look and texture can use a chopped cucumber or jicama and spice up soup with some cayenne pepper.

INGREDIENTS

4	soup bones
2	pounds stew beef
1	chopped onion
4	chopped carrots
1	tbsp seasoning salt
4	chopped celery stalks
4	chopped zucchini
3	ears of corn cut in half
1	daikon radish chopped
1	small cabbage in wedges
10	cups of water or low sodium beef stock

DIRECTIONS 8 SERVINGS

1. Add bones and beef and onion and seasoning salt, cover with water or stock.
2. Cook in a covered pot till beef is tender (about 2 hours).
3. Take out bones and chopped veggies and cook additional 10 minutes.
4. Add cabbage and cook 10 minutes more.
5. Turn off stove keep covered additional 45 minutes and serve.

FOODMOVER WINDOWS TO CLOSE PER SERVING

NUTRITION INFORMATION PER SERVING	
CALORIES	231
PROTEIN	31g
CARBOHYDRATE	14g
TOTAL FAT	6g
SODIUM	102mg

42ND STREET EGG ROLLS
BY FAITH HORAN

"I tried the Weight Watchers program and it was too complicated. The FoodMover is easy and pain free. I love it!"

ONE-TWO-THREE DIP
BY MASON SCHWALM

I'm 12 years old and I made this recipe for a Richard Simmons' Angel picnic. Everyone liked my recipe so I wanted all of you to try it and hopefully you'll like it too. Since my mom has been using the FoodMover, I am learning that I can have some low-fat food instead of junk and it still tastes good.

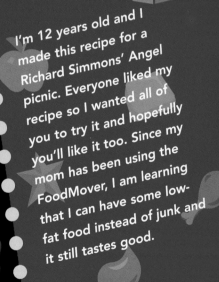

ANNIE GET YOUR CORN BUNS

BY CHRISTINA BROWN

Tip: I love these; they're so cute. Why no protein window? There is so little turkey in each one it wasn't even enough to close any window.

INGREDIENTS

One small box (8.5 oz) of corn muffin mix (mixed with skim milk and egg substitute)

1/8 pound honey roasted turkey cut into small round pieces about the size of a dime

1/2 cup cranberry sauce

cooking spray

DIRECTIONS — 12 APPETIZERS/SERVING SIZE 1 MUFFIN

1. Prepare corn muffin mix and bake in mini muffin pan sprayed with cooking spray till just cooked.
2. Cool muffins, cut in half and spread with cranberry sauce, turkey put on top and serve.

FOODMOVER WINDOWS TO CLOSE PER SERVING

NUTRITION INFORMATION PER SERVING	
CALORIES	76
PROTEIN	3.3g
CARBOHYDRATE	13g
TOTAL FAT	1.2g
SODIUM	108mg

42ND STREET EGG ROLLS

4TH PRIZE

BY FAITH HORAN

INGREDIENTS

- 2.5 cups coleslaw
- 1/2 cup shredded carrots
- 1/2 cup chopped mushrooms
- 1 tbsp chopped scallions
- 2 eggs, beaten
- 1 oz low sodium soy sauce
- 12 egg roll wrappers
- Buttery Pam

Serve with Colman's mustard on the side (YUM)

DIRECTIONS 12 (ONE EGG ROLL) SERVINGS

1. Combine coleslaw, carrots, mushrooms, scallions, beaten eggs, and soy sauce.
2. Fill egg roll wrappers and roll.
3. Spray with Buttery Pam.
4. Bake in 400° oven until golden brown, about 20 minutes.

Tip: Egg roll wrappers are found in most supermarkets in cold section of the produce department. Keep them refrigerated until ready to use. Tastes great with hot and spicy mustard for dipping! Colman's mustard is used in a lot of Asian dishes.

FOODMOVER WINDOWS TO CLOSE PER SERVING

NUTRITION INFORMATION PER SERVING	
CALORIES	112
PROTEIN	1.5g
CARBOHYDRATE	22g
TOTAL FAT	2g
SODIUM	625mg

ONE, TWO, THREE, DIP!

BY MASON SCHWALM

Tip: If you serve with crackers or baked chips make sure you close additional windows.

(This is one of my favorites. It reminds me of the one made in the '50s with dry soup mix.)

INGREDIENTS

- 8 oz low fat cream cheese
- 8 oz low fat sour cream
- 1 tsp garlic powder
- 2 tbsp roasted dried onions
- 3 tsp onion powder
- 2 finely diced scallions
- 1/2 cup chopped white onion
- 1/4 cup water
- cooking spray

DIRECTIONS 12 (3 TABLESPOON) SERVINGS

1. Spray cooking spray in skillet and sauté white onions in water until soft, cool.
2. Mix with remaining ingredients.
3. Serve with veggies or crackers.

FOODMOVER WINDOWS TO CLOSE PER SERVING

NUTRITION INFORMATION PER SERVING	
CALORIES	75
PROTEIN	3g
CARBOHYDRATE	7.5g
TOTAL FAT	4.5g
SODIUM	306mg

OVATION ONION RINGS

BY DARLENE FOSTER

INGREDIENTS

1/2 vidalia onion
1/4 cup Egg Beaters
1/4 cup all purpose flour
1/2 cup corn flakes cereal
1 tsp cayenne pepper
(optional; live a little)
Pam olive oil cooking spray

DIRECTIONS [2 SERVINGS]

1. Preheat oven to 475°, preheat un-prepared pan.
2. Slice onion and separate into rings.
3. Dip rings into Egg Beaters, then very lightly in the flour, cayenne pepper, then in the crushed cornflakes. Only if needed, you may dip in Egg Beaters a second time between flour and cornflakes.
4. Spray heated pan with Pam and spread rings onto cookie sheet in a single layer. Spray tops of onion rings with Pam.
5. Place in hot oven and bake until golden and crispy. Serve immediately.

Tip: These onion rings are crispy and light; you won't believe that they have no fat. I have no doubt that you will give this recipe a standing ovation. You can get Vidalia onions in most supermarkets or they can be ordered through a mail order catalog. Corn flakes work best in this recipe but you can use other flake cereals or even bread crumbs if you want to.

FOODMOVER WINDOWS TO CLOSE PER SERVING

NUTRITION INFORMATION PER SERVING	
CALORIES	102
PROTEIN	5g
CARBOHYDRATE	19g
TOTAL FAT	0g
SODIUM	111mg

SHRIMP DE-LIGHTS ON BROADWAY

BY KATHLEEN RISK

Tip: Neufchatel cheese is not a city in Norway, it's a low fat type of cream cheese that you can find in your supermarket dairy section.

INGREDIENTS

- 8 oz Neufchatel cheese (low fat cream cheese)
- 2 oz large chopped cooked shrimp
- 2 tbsp chopped onions
- 2 tbsp Worcestershire sauce
- 1 tsp lemon juice
- 1 tsp cocktail sauce
- 7 whole wheat pita bread
- 20 red bell pepper strips
- 20 green olive slices
- 1 tbsp chopped parsley

DIRECTIONS 20 (6 ITEM) SERVINGS

1. Stir cream cheese to soften.
2. Mix in chopped shrimp, onion, Worcestershire sauce, lemon juice, and cocktail sauce.
3. Cut pita bread into small triangles and bake until crisp.
4. Spoon a teaspoon of mixture on each triangle and garnish with a strip of red pepper and a slice of green olive.
5. Garnish with chopped parsley.

FOODMOVER WINDOWS TO CLOSE PER SERVING

NUTRITION INFORMATION PER SERVING	
CALORIES	94
PROTEIN	4g
CARBOHYDRATE	13g
TOTAL FAT	3g
SODIUM	193mg

This recipe has been a favorite in our family for more than 15 years. "The FoodMover gives me a quick visual reference for keeping up with my eating for the day. I have used an exchange diet before but I had to keep a food journal and a tally sheet. Sometimes it was difficult to see at a glance what choices to make with my eating. With the FoodMover, I just glance and see what windows are left open and I know immediately what I can eat. It's so easy. I just love opening all the windows each morning. It's like a metaphor for opening myself up to all the possibilities to have a wonderful day."

UPSTAGE THE BUN! HAMBURGER SALAD
BY CHERYL WILLIAMS

KICKIN' CHICKEN SALAD
BY KELLY LUCAS

"I've lost 25 lbs in 2 1/2 months. Since I started the FoodMover and the videos, my energy has skyrocketed! I know when to stop eating and I never feel the need to finish all the food on my plate. I know I will reach my goal and even when I do the FoodMover will always be a part of my life. The FoodMover was the best investment of my life."

BROADWAY BONUS (A FREEBIE SALAD)

BY RICHARD SIMMONS

Tip: This is what I eat when listening to all those Broadway show tunes! Get this- all the ingredients are under the Bonus section of my exchange booklets. Who said the best things in life aren't free? You don't have to open and close any windows! You just have to open and close your mouth. This salad is the zenith of roughage- the pinnacle of greenery! It's my own personal recommendation to eat this at least 1x a week!

Tip: on roasting Garlic. Let me tell you something- once you roast garlic you'll never go back! And guess what? Roasted garlic doesn't leave as much odor. So enjoy the taste of garlic without the odoriferous smell. To roast garlic, cut off the pointed side of the head exposing the cloves, spray lightly with cooking spray, wrap in aluminum foil and bake in a 350° oven for about 1 hour until soft and caramelized.

INGREDIENTS

- 2 cups assorted mixed lettuce (mesculin)
- 1 cup alfalfa sprouts (optional)
- 1/2 cup chopped red cabbage
- 1/2 cup chopped or sliced cucumber
- 1/2 cup shredded zucchini
- 1/2 cup sliced mushrooms
- 1/4 cup chopped tomato
- 2 tbsp chopped red onion
- 4 roasted cloves of garlic
- 1/8 cup balsamic vinegar
- 2 tbsp chopped favorite herbs
- salt an pepper to taste

DIRECTIONS 2 SERVINGS

1. Combine all ingredients together.
2. Chill and enjoy.

FOODMOVER WINDOWS TO CLOSE PER SERVING	NUTRITION INFORMATION PER SERVING	
	CALORIES	39
	PROTEIN	2.3g
NO WINDOWS	CARBOHYDRATE	7.9g
	TOTAL FAT	0g
	SODIUM	140mg

KICKIN' CHICKEN SALAD

BY KELLY LUCAS

INGREDIENTS

- 2 oz poached chicken sliced
- 1 oz shredded part-skim mozzarella cheese
- 3 tbsp fat-free croutons
- 2 cups romaine lettuce or mixed chopped greens
- 1 medium chopped tomato
- 1/2 cup cauliflower chopped
- 1 chopped cucumber
- 4 sliced radishes
- 2 tbsp fat-free italian dressing

DIRECTIONS 1 SERVINGS

1. Mix chopped veggies together and place chicken on top.
2. Sprinkle with cheese, croutons and salad dressing.

Tip: To poach chicken, lightly simmer water or low sodium chicken stock, add chicken and poach till chicken is just cooked, white through when cut.

To make your own fat-free croutons cut bread into small pieces, spray with cooking spray lightly and bake in a 350° oven until crispy.

FOODMOVER WINDOWS TO CLOSE PER SERVING

NUTRITION INFORMATION PER SERVING	
CALORIES	245
PROTEIN	22g
CARBOHYDRATE	17g
TOTAL FAT	10g
SODIUM	375mg

OPENING NUMBER ANTIPASTO DELIGHT

BY TIFFANI SCHULTE

Tip: Grill veggies by cleaning, drying and slightly spraying with cooking spray. Place on hot grill and grill until softened and grill marks visible. Can be done on stove top in a grill pan as well.

INGREDIENTS

- 8 cups torn salad greens (romaine)
- 8 2" slices roasted red pepper (In natural juices)
- 1 small onion (thinly sliced)
- 2 cups mixed grilled veggies (mushrooms, onions, zucchini and eggplant)
- 4 oz drained artichoke hearts (in natural juices)
- 16 black olives
- 4 oz part-skim mozzarella cheese, cut into strips
- 8 tbsp fat-free Wishbone Italian dressing

DIRECTIONS 4 SERVINGS

1. Spray non-stick fry pan with butter flavor cooking spray.
2. Add onions, spray with cooking spray. Add scant amount of water.
3. Cover pan and place over medium heat. Stir occasionally until slightly tender. Add grilled veggies, artichoke hearts and olives. Heat 1 more minute. Let cool.
4. Add all ingredients together. Toss and enjoy! (No one will know it's not the real thing...it tastes like it was marinating all day!) Can be served arranged over the bed of greens as well.

FOODMOVER WINDOWS TO CLOSE PER SERVING

NUTRITION INFORMATION PER SERVING	
CALORIES	204
PROTEIN	9.5g
CARBOHYDRATE	21.75g
TOTAL FAT	6.7g
SODIUM	917mg

UPSTAGE THE BUN! HAMBURGER SALAD

BY CHERYL WILLIAMS

INGREDIENTS

- 1 pound lean ground sirloin beef
- 1 onion, chopped
- 1 tbsp lite Worcestershire sauce
- 1 head lettuce (broken into lettuce cups
- 1 cup pickles (chopped like relish)
- 2 tomatoes, diced fine

jalapeno peppers, if you like it hot

pepper to taste

Dressing:
- 4 tbsp mustard (Colman's or dijon or honey mustard your choice) (optional)
- 4 tbsp catsup

DIRECTIONS 4 SERVINGS

1. Brown one pound of extra lean ground beef until crumbly with one chopped onion.
2. Season with pepper and Worcestershire. Drain well and set aside on paper plate or paper towels to remove excess fat.
3. Serve lettuce cups with toppings on the side for desired stuffing.

Tip: Excellent if all the toppings are arranged on a platter with lettuce cups. Stuff each lettuce cup and roll. To make lettuce cups, you cut, core, and stack, then ziplock to keep moist. Refrigerate until ready to serve.

FOODMOVER WINDOWS TO CLOSE PER SERVING

NUTRITION INFORMATION PER SERVING	
CALORIES	210
PROTEIN	29.7g
CARBOHYDRATE	4g
TOTAL FAT	7.8g
SODIUM	723mg

CAMELOT'S CHICKEN
BY STACIE KELLEY

"I've lost 40 lbs on the FoodMover Program. I don't feel sluggish anymore. Now I can keep up with my four extremely active children."

JAZZY TAPPIN' BROCCOLI
BY GALE QUINN

"Thank you so much Richard for helping me to see my faults in my diet and guiding me to success through proper eating habits and more importantly, proper amounts in each category of foods. The FoodMover makes it easy to see just what you are eating so you know you are balancing your diet. I couldn't do it without the FoodMover to guide me."

CLAMS AT SEA

BY NORINNE WILSON

INGREDIENTS

- 1 tbsp olive oil
- 1/2 chopped onion
- 4 thinly sliced garlic cloves
- 2 7 oz canned or fresh chopped clams
- 8 fluid oz clam juice
- 1 14 oz can low sodium chicken stock
- 6 sprigs fresh thyme
- 2 chopped plum tomatoes
- 4 cups cooked spaghetti
- 4 tbsp shredded Parmesan
- 1 tsp pepper
- 1/2 tsp salt
- pinch of red chili pepper

DIRECTIONS — 4 SERVINGS

1. Slice garlic cloves thin. Sauté garlic in olive oil and then add chopped onion and sauté until tender, but do not brown.
2. Add clams, tomatoes, and hot pepper flakes (some like it hot), thyme clam juice, chicken stock.
3. Simmer for 15 minutes until flavors are blended and liquid slightly reduced.
4. Serve over cooked pasta; top with shredded Parmesan.

Tip: Use clams in their own juices; you can also find chopped clams in the freezer section. Looking for an alternative to Parmesan, why don't you try Romano or Reggiano; I have the inside scoop that this is what the Pope uses.

FOODMOVER WINDOWS TO CLOSE PER SERVING

NUTRITION INFORMATION PER SERVING	
CALORIES	323
PROTEIN	17g
CARBOHYDRATE	48g
TOTAL FAT	7g
SODIUM	900mg

ON YOUR MARK PASTA

BY JEANETTE BELAND

Tip: Extra virgin first pressed olive oil is darker green and has an excellent flavor. Lite olive oil is light in color and flavor but has the same amount of fat.

Wondering where capers come from? Capers grow mostly in the tropics with many coming from Africa, Australia and Asia.

INGREDIENTS

2	cups cooked pasta (capellini/angel hair)
3	artichoke hearts, cut-up (fresh/frozen, not marinated)
1	tbsp capers
2	tsp basil
2	tsp oregano
1	tsp pepper
1	cup cherry tomatoes, halved (or vine ripened; they taste better)
1-1/2	tsp chopped garlic
3	scallions, cut into small pieces
1-1/2	tbsp extra virgin olive oil
2	oz finely grated Romano cheese (optional)

cooking spray
Sea salt (small pinch)
fresh basil for garnish (optional)

DIRECTIONS 2 SERVINGS

1. Spray skillet with cooking spray and heat.
2. Sauté the garlic and onions for a minute or two.
3. Add in the artichoke hearts, capers, and cherry tomatoes and olive oil.
4. Sauté for 2-3 minutes.
5. Add the basil, oregano, pepper, and salt.
6. Add pasta and mix well.
7. Top with Romano cheese.
8. Garnish with fresh basil, if desired.

FOODMOVER WINDOWS TO CLOSE PER SERVING

(Without Romano Cheese)

(With Romano Cheese)

NUTRITION INFORMATION PER SERVING		
	Without Cheese	With Cheese
CALORIES	333	442
PROTEIN	8.8g	17.9g
CARBOHYDRATE	50g	51g
TOTAL FAT	11.7g	19g
SODIUM	484mg	842mg

JAZZY TAPPIN' BROCCOLI (BROCCOLI AND PASTA)

BY GALE QUINN

INGREDIENTS

- 8 oz linguini pasta
- 1-2 cloves fresh garlic, minced
- 1 tbsp extra virgin olive oil
- 1/4 tsp black pepper
- 1 cup nonfat milk
- 2 cups fresh broccoli blossoms, rinsed and drained
- 2 tbsp cornstarch
- parsley sprigs (for decorating stage!)

DIRECTIONS 4 SERVINGS

1. Prepare pasta according to package in a medium sized pan.
2. Rinse pasta with hot water, then cool water to remove excess starch.
3. Drain pasta and arrange in a serving dish.
4. While pasta is cooking, sauté garlic in olive oil for about 1 minute (sing a little song while you stir!).
5. Add fresh broccoli, stir and cover to steam for about 4 minutes, or until broccoli is brilliant green and jazzy! You may need to add a tablespoon or two of water during this act.
6. For the finale, get those feet and fingers tapping to a mixture of milk, cornstarch and pepper combined in a small pot. Mix well and stir over medium heat until the plot thickens.
7. Add creamy mixture to broccoli and conclude by placing the broccoli to bed over linguini.
8. Arrange parsley to dress up the stage and enjoy.
9. Serve immediately with side show salad.

Tip: There are different types of parsley, curly and flat leaf. I like to use the curly for garnishing and the flat leaf to chop. If you're allergic to corn starch why not try arrowroot instead, available in most stores.

FOODMOVER WINDOWS TO CLOSE PER SERVING

NUTRITION INFORMATION PER SERVING	
CALORIES	289
PROTEIN	11g
CARBOHYDRATE	50g
TOTAL FAT	5g
SODIUM	118mg

"I've lost over 55lbs on the program. I am a new person with more energy and a zest for life. I love you Richard."

SOUTH PACIFIC CHICKEN
BY CHAD CALAWAY

"This is a healthy and tasty recipe. My family loves it, so I wanted to share it with you and hopefully all your friends. I am very confident that I will reach my goal weight with the FoodMover program. Weight has been a problem of mine since the 5th grade. I know I can do it with Richard's help."

CAMELOT'S CHICKEN

BY STACIE KELLEY

INGREDIENTS

- 2 10 oz frozen pkg. drained artichoke hearts (frozen artichokes need to be defrosted and drained for best results)
- 2 cups cooked (cut into bite size chunks) chicken breast
- 1/2 cup low fat shredded cheddar cheese
- 1/4 cup chopped green onions
- 1/4 cup Parmesan cheese
- 1/4 cup bread crumbs
- 1/2 cup skim milk
- 1/2 cup Egg Beaters
- 1 tbsp chopped parsley
- 1/2 tsp salt
- 1 tsp paprika
- 1/2 tsp dried rosemary
- 2 tbsp sliced almonds

DIRECTIONS [4 SERVINGS]

1. Mix chicken, spices, green onions and artichokes together.
2. Layer chicken mixture in a baking dish with cheddar and bread crumbs, Parmesan about 2 layers topping off with breadcrumbs and Parmesan.
3. Mix Egg Beaters and milk and pour over casserole.
4. Top with almonds and bake covered in a 350° oven for about 30 minutes until bubbly and the chicken is cooked through.
5. Optional: can garnish with cherry tomatoes and chives.

Tip: Frozen artichokes need to be defrosted and drained for best results.

Tip: If you want to make your own bread crumbs use either stale bread or fresh toasted bread. Run bread through a food processor till desired consistency. Can be made stuffed into steamed artichokes as well.

FOODMOVER WINDOWS TO CLOSE PER SERVING

NUTRITION INFORMATION PER SERVING	
CALORIES	339
PROTEIN	43.2g
CARBOHYDRATE	22g
TOTAL FAT	9.3g
SODIUM	762mg

FLOWER DRUM RICE

BY DONNA MCCRORY

Tip: Run measuring cup under hot water before adding honey. It will make it easier to get the honey out of the cup. Ginger is a great seasoning agent used in most Asian cooking; you can buy it ground but it is even better if you buy the fresh root and grate it up.

INGREDIENTS

- 12 oz chicken breasts (boneless, skinless)
- 1 pound snow peapods
- 1 can sliced waterchestnuts (drained)
- 4 cloves garlic, crushed
- 1/2 tsp ground ginger
- 2 cups chicken broth low sodium
- 1/2 cup honey
- 2 tbsp cornstarch
- 1 lime
- 2 tbsp lite soy sauce
- 2 cups cooked rice
- 1/2 cup shredded carrots
- 1/2 cup chopped red pepper
- 2 sliced scallions
- non-stick cooking spray
- pinch dry mustard

DIRECTIONS 4 SERVINGS

1. Cut chicken into bite sized pieces. Spray pan with non-stick cooking spray.
2. Lightly brown chicken pieces in skillet, approximately 5 minutes.
3. Add chicken broth, snow peapods and water chestnuts. Cover and simmer until chicken is cooked through, approximately 10 minutes. Stir occasionally.
4. While chicken is cooking, in a bowl combine honey, 2 tablespoons gated lime peel, juice from lime, garlic, ginger, dry mustard and cornstarch. Whisk together until well mixed.
5. When chicken is cooked through, pour honey mixture over chicken into skillet. Cook, stirring constantly, until thickened. Cook rice with carrots and peppers.
6. Divide chicken over rice.
7. Garnish with sliced scallions.

FOODMOVER WINDOWS TO CLOSE PER SERVING

NUTRITION INFORMATION PER SERVING	
CALORIES	457
PROTEIN	33.7g
CARBOHYDRATE	59.4g
TOTAL FAT	9.6g
SODIUM	670mg

I'M JUST WILD ABOUT CHICKEN ENCHILADAS

BY LAURIE EGGLEZOS

INGREDIENTS

- 1/2 pound shredded cooked white meat chicken
- 1/8 cup low sodium chicken stock
- 4 6" tortillas shells (soft flour)
- 1 small chopped onion
- 1 chopped red pepper
- 2 tsp minced garlic
- 4 oz low fat cheddar
- 8 oz enchilada sauce
- cooking spray
- optional garnish leaf lettuce, chopped tomato and dill pepper

DIRECTIONS 4 SERVINGS

1. Spray cooking spray in skillet and sauté onions and garlic and peppers until onions are translucent and peppers are soft.
2. Stir in chicken and stock and heat until almost all stock is evaporated.
3. Put about 1/4 filling in each tortilla and roll seam side down. Place in oven proof dish.
4. Top with enchilada sauce and shredded cheese and bake in 350° oven about 10 minutes until cheese is melted and sauce is hot and bubbly.
5. Serve with optional lettuce, chopped tomato and dill pepper.

Tip: There are many different types of enchilada sauce available in your supermarket, usually in the ethnic aisle. Try to choose one without any added fat.

FOODMOVER WINDOWS TO CLOSE PER SERVING

NUTRITION INFORMATION PER SERVING	
CALORIES	272
PROTEIN	26g
CARBOHYDRATE	25.4g
TOTAL FAT	6g
SODIUM	532mg

3RD PRIZE — SHOW STOPPER ITALIAN CHICKEN AND ORZO

BY LINDA HOLBROOK

Tip: Orzo is a pasta that looks like fat rice. Cook and serve.

INGREDIENTS

- 4 chicken breast or tenderloins, 3 oz each servings
- 1 cup chopped onion
- 1 package fresh spinach (chopped)
- 1 tsp garlic powder
- 1/2 tsp cumin
- 1/2 cup chicken broth (fat free)
- 1/2 cup balsamic vinegar
- 6 oz can tomato paste
- 4 tsp margarine
- 4 tbsp brown sugar
- 8 tbsp Parmesan cheese
- 4 cups cooked orzo

DIRECTIONS — 4 SERVINGS

1. Sprinkle chicken with pepper and brown on each side in a non-stick pan with a small amount of water. Remove and set aside.

2. In a large skillet over medium heat; melt margarine. Sauté onion and spinach until reduced.

3. Add garlic powder, cumin, chicken broth, wine, tomato paste, and sugar. Stir together all ingredients until the sauce is smooth. If the sauce is too thick add up to 3/4 cup of water to thin it, and simmer with a lid on for 10 minutes.

4. In a 9x12 baking dish ladle enough sauce to cover the bottom of the dish; put cooked orzo and top with chicken and remaining sauce.

5. Sprinkle 8 tbsp Parmesan cheese evenly over the top. Cover with foil and bake at 350° for 25 minutes.

6. Remove foil and bake for additional 10 minutes. Remove from oven and serve.

FOODMOVER WINDOWS TO CLOSE PER SERVING

NUTRITION INFORMATION PER SERVING	
CALORIES	380
PROTEIN	24g
CARBOHYDRATE	43g
TOTAL FAT	11g
SODIUM	950mg

SMOKEY JOE'S TURKEY MEATLOAF

BY HELEN MARBELL

INGREDIENTS

- 2 pound ground turkey
- 1/2 cup instant oatmeal
- 1 cup chopped onion
- 1 cup tomato sauce
- 2 tsp minced garlic
- 2 tsp Italian seasoning
- 1/2 tsp salt
- 1/4 cup Egg Beaters
- 6 slices turkey bacon
- cooking spray
- pepper to taste

DIRECTIONS 8 SERVINGS

1. Spray skillet with cooking spray and brown onions.
2. In a large bowl mix onion, meat, tomato sauce, egg and seasonings.
3. Spray a loaf pan with cooking spray and fill with meat mixture; top mixture with turkey bacon slices.
4. Bake in 350° oven for about 1 hour and 45 minutes until the meat is browned and shrinks from the sides of the pan.

Tip: The oatmeal holds this meatloaf together and provides moisture. Turkey bacon is usually lower in fat than other types of bacon. If turkey bacon is unavailable try to use another reduced fat bacon. Serve with steamed vegetables.

FOODMOVER WINDOWS TO CLOSE PER SERVING

NUTRITION INFORMATION PER SERVING	
CALORIES	245
PROTEIN	23.5g
CARBOHYDRATE	10.3g
TOTAL FAT	12g
SODIUM	665mg

1ST PRIZE

SOUTH PACIFIC CHICKEN

BY CHAD CALAWAY

Tip: There are many spice rub mixes available at your supermarket which can be used when you don't have the time to mix your own spices. A good combo would be a pumpkin spice mix and you add garlic, pepper salt and brown sugar. The secret is in the rub. Not closing any additional fat windows for the fat is represented in the protein windows. Great served with mixed green salad.

INGREDIENTS

4 cups low sodium chicken broth
1 tbsp olive oil
1 chopped onion
1 chopped garlic clove
1 peeled and chopped mango
2 tbsp brown sugar
1/2 cup white wine (don't worry you won't get tipsy in the south pacific)
1 tbsp olive oil
4 chicken breasts (boneless, skinless)

Spice Rub

2 tsp cinnamon
2 tsp chili powder
2 tsp ground ginger
1 tsp ground cloves
2 tsp garlic powder
1 tsp ground allspice
2 tsp brown sugar
1 tsp kosher salt
2 tsp black pepper
1 tsp red or cayenne pepper

DIRECTIONS 4 (1 BREAST WITH APPROXIMATELY 1/2 CUP MANGO SAUCE) SERVINGS

1. Preheat oven to 350°. Put chicken broth in a saucepan over medium high heat, and reduce by half.
2. In a separate skillet heat the olive oil and sweat the onion until soft, approximately 20 minutes. Add the brown sugar, stock, salt and pepper, mango, mix well. Cook until mango is soft, approximately 20 minutes.
3. Place the mixture in a blender and puree until smooth. Strain mixture back into saucepan, and cook for 10-12 minutes until reduced and thickened.
4. While cooking mango mixture, mix all spices together in a bowl.
5. Brush each side of chicken with olive oil, and coat with the spices. Place in a hot, ovenproof sauté pan, and sear on each side.
6. Pour in 1/2 cup of wine to deglaze pan, cover with foil, and place in oven for 25-30 minutes, until done.
7. Place 1 piece of chicken on each plate, and pour mango sauce on each piece.

FOODMOVER WINDOWS TO CLOSE PER SERVING

NUTRITION INFORMATION PER SERVING	
CALORIES	280
PROTEIN	25g
CARBOHYDRATE	25g
TOTAL FAT	11g
SODIUM	856mg

"With our busy family of college kids and work, we have little time to remember what we ate at our last meal. The FoodMover is an excellent tool to remind and guide our daily meal plan."

"The FoodMover is easy. I have better eating habits and finally I'm seeing results with weight-loss."

FOOD REVIEW

It's A Hit, Critics Say!

Whatta Meatball!

-Opening Act
Antipasta Salad
-Critics Choice
Meatballs
Curtain Call
Pistachio Pie

BEEFY SECOND ACT

BY NICOLE CLARK

Tip: To get bouillon cubes to dissolve faster add a little bit of boiling water to the cubes first before adding to other ingredients. Fat is counted here in the protein windows.

INGREDIENTS

12	oz very lean ground beef
1/4	cup chopped onions
2	cups chopped tomato
1	chopped green bell pepper
2	15 oz cans whole kernel corn (drained)
1	cup water
2-1/2	cup uncooked long grain rice
2	low sodium beef bouillon cubes (can use 1 cup of low sodium beef broth if you omit the bouillon cubes and 1 cup of water)
1	tsp garlic

DIRECTIONS 6 (1-1/2 CUP) SERVINGS

1. Brown meat with onion. Drain and rinse with water.
2. Place in skillet and add tomato, corn, green pepper, garlic, water, and beef cubes. Simmer 30 to 40 minutes on low heat.
3. When tomato is tender, turn off the heat and add instant rice cover 5 minutes then serve. Salt and pepper to taste.
4. Optional garnish with red and green pepper slices.

FOODMOVER WINDOWS TO CLOSE PER SERVING

NUTRITION INFORMATION PER SERVING	
CALORIES	410
PROTEIN	24g
CARBOHYDRATE	56g
TOTAL FAT	11.6g
SODIUM	641mg

DISAPPEARING ACT CHILI

BY JOSEPH ARLUKIEWICZ

INGREDIENTS

2	tbsp olive oil
2	pounds very lean ground beef
1-1/2	chopped onions
2	chopped garlic cloves
1-1/2	tbsp ground cumin
2	28 oz can diced Tomatoes in Juice
1	15 oz can dark red kidney beans
1	15 oz can pinto beans
2	chopped jalapeno peppers
2	tbsp pepper sauce (tabasco) optional
2	tsp salt
1/2	cup low fat shredded cheddar

DIRECTIONS 8 (1 CUP) SERVINGS

1. Heat oil in 5-quart pot over medium heat. Add beef and cook until well browned; remove from heat to another bowl with slotted spoon to keep drippings in pot.

2. Add onion and garlic to drippings, and cook over medium heat about 5 minutes or until slightly opaque.

3. Return meat to pot and add cumin. Cook for another 5 minutes to blend.

4. Then stir in diced tomatoes, with their liquid, pinto beans, kidney beans, green chilies, hot sauce, and salt. Heat to boiling over high heat. Reduce heat to low and let simmer for about 30 - 60 minutes, depending on consistency, stirring occasionally.

5. Serve each cup of chili with 1 tbsp of the shredded cheddar.

Tip: Jalapeno peppers are available in most supermarkets. Tabasco Sauce comes from Louisiana where Richard is from (probably why he is sooo sassy). Don't worry about not closing any fat windows; they are there in the protein.

FOODMOVER WINDOWS TO CLOSE PER SERVING

NUTRITION INFORMATION PER SERVING	
CALORIES	365
PROTEIN	42.1g
CARBOHYDRATE	18.9g
TOTAL FAT	12.6g
SODIUM	1157mg

MISS SAIGON BEEF AND CASHEWS SALAD

BY JODI WRIGHT

Tip: Although cashews are high in fat we only used a little to give you that great cashew flavor. Canola oil is a good fat to use in stir fries; it has a high smoking point so it doesn't break down easily and is high in monounsaturated fatty acids (a better fat to use).

INGREDIENTS

2	cups chopped iceberg lettuce
1/2	pound beef tenderloin cut into 2" pieces
1/8	cup canola oil
1	tsp sesame oil
1	tsp minced fresh ginger
1	tbsp chopped garlic
2	tbsp lite soy sauce
1	tsp sugar
2	tbsp hoisin sauce
1	peeled chopped cucumber
1/4	cup chopped cashews
6	chopped green onions
cayenne pepper to taste	

DIRECTIONS 4 SERVINGS

1. Heat oil and sauté onion and garlic.
2. Add beef and cashews and heat until cooked.
3. Add cucumbers and all other ingredients until heated through.
4. Serve over salad greens.
5. Optional can garnish with cucumber and radishes.

FOODMOVER WINDOWS TO CLOSE PER SERVING

NUTRITION INFORMATION PER SERVING	
CALORIES	249
PROTEIN	19.8g
CARBOHYDRATE	6.3g
TOTAL FAT	16.23g
SODIUM	689mg

STUFFY CRITICS CHOICE MEATBALLS

2ND PRIZE

BY TIFFANI SCHULTE

INGREDIENTS

- 1 pound ground turkey breast
- 1 egg
- 1/2 cup quick cooking oats
- 1/2 cup onion, finely chopped
- 1 tsp salt
- 1/2 cup loosely packed brown sugar
- 1 tsp mustard
- 8 tbsp or 1/2 cup ketchup
- 6 oz low fat mozzarella cut into cubes

DIRECTIONS 8 (2 MEATBALLS) SERVINGS

1. In a large mixing bowl, combine ground turkey, egg, oats, salt and onion.
2. Mix well and form into 16 meatballs by forming meat around a chunk of mozzarella cheese, slightly indent tops.
3. Place on a baking dish.
4. In a separate bowl, mix brown sugar, mustard and ketchup.
5. Spoon evenly over meatballs.
6. Bake uncovered at 350° for 45 minutes.

Tip: You could make smaller meatballs and use as a party appetizer. You will hear the "ahhs" when your family and friends cut into the meatballs and see the cheese oozing. Meatballs can also be served over 1/2 cup cooked pasta for an additional starch window.

FOODMOVER WINDOWS TO CLOSE PER SERVING

NUTRITION INFORMATION PER SERVING	
CALORIES	185
PROTEIN	14g
CARBOHYDRATE	15g
TOTAL FAT	7g
SODIUM	330mg

MEMORIES "SWEET AND SOUR" PEPPER STEAK

BY ANN BROWN

Tip: Molasses is the syrup remaining after sugar is crystallized out of cane or beet juice. This syrup is cultivated and processed to give us different grades of molasses. Only one fat window is closed because the rest of the fat is represented in the protein window.

INGREDIENTS

- 14 oz lean steak cut into 2" long pieces cut on an angle (against the grain)
- 2 large sliced onions
- 2 large sliced red peppers
- 1/2 cup pineapple chunks in their own juice drained
- 1 tbsp garlic
- 2 tbsp molasses
- 1 tbsp lemon juice
- 2 beef bouillon cubes & 1/8 cup water
- 1 tbsp corn starch with 2 tbsp water
- 1 tbsp Olive oil
- 2 tbsp Lite soy sauce

pepper to taste
scallions for garnish

DIRECTIONS 4 SERVINGS

1. Heat oil in a large non stick skillet and brown garlic.

2. Add onions and peppers and sauté until onions are translucent.

3. Add beef, molasses, lemon juice, beef bouillon cubes, water and soy sauce. Cover and simmer about 20 minutes.

4. Stir in pineapple and corn starch mixture, heat through 5 more minutes uncovered or until thickened and serve (garnish with scallions).

FOODMOVER WINDOWS TO CLOSE PER SERVING

NUTRITION INFORMATION PER SERVING	
CALORIES	342
PROTEIN	21g
CARBOHYDRATE	19.6g
TOTAL FAT	19.9g
SODIUM	407mg

"I make this recipe for me and my husband once a week. We both love it. The FoodMover has made me aware of my portion sizes and has taught me that eating 6 small meals a day is a way to never feel deprived or hungry. I have noticed that I feel a lot better eating 6 smaller meals as opposed to eating 2 huge meals a day. I would feel sluggish and overstuffed. I have also been drinking a lot of water which I had never done before. Not only do I feel good, my skin looks great and so do I."

STANDING OVATION SHRIMP SCAMPI
BY TERI STONE

SEAFOOD SHOWBOAT
BY JENNIFER BROSS

"The FoodMover is the only program that makes sense. It's a wonderful program because it teaches you how to gradually eat less. It's a smart idea. I think the biggest thing it does for me is to get me to eat healthier and to control my portions. I don't feel guilty at the end of the day. I can keep track of my water. It reminds me to exercise and take my vitamins too."

LITTLE MERMAIDS SALMON SPECIAL

BY TOM ESTMAN

Tip: I've got a secret. If you've always thought that salmon was a little too fishy for your gills... Well, guess what? The lime juice in this recipe cuts out any fishy taste. PS: No fat window; the fat is in the protein.

INGREDIENTS

- 8 oz salmon filet
- 2 tsp minced garlic
- 1/4 cup seasoned bread crumbs
- 1 tbsp Parmesan cheese
- 1/2 tsp dill
- 1/2 cup chicken stock
- 1/4 cup lime juice
- optional lime wedges and dill garnish

DIRECTIONS 2 SERVINGS

1. In a skillet sear salmon on both sides in olive oil 2-3 minutes.
2. Turn off heat; add minced garlic.
3. Transfer to casserole dish and add chicken stock to bottom of dish.
4. Sprinkle with dill and bake in 350° oven for 15 minutes until cooked.
5. Pour on lime juice.
6. Serve with lime wedges and fresh dill.
7. Bake in 350° oven until salmon flakes easily about 15-20 minutes.

FOODMOVER WINDOWS TO CLOSE PER SERVING

NUTRITION INFORMATION PER SERVING	
CALORIES	226
PROTEIN	25.3g
CARBOHYDRATE	9.8g
TOTAL FAT	9.2g
SODIUM	375mg

MY ONE AND ONLY FISH

BY PATRICIA STEWART

INGREDIENTS

- 2 tbsp minced garlic
- 1/3 cup chopped green onions
- 1 cup chopped red peppers
- 1 cup chopped celery
- 1 tbsp chopped fresh oregano
- 15 oz can stewed tomatoes with onion, celery and green pepper
- 3 tbsp red wine vinegar (there are also some great new white balsamic vinegars to try)
- 2 pounds sea bass fillets (If sea bass is not available swordfish works well in this recipe as well)
- olive oil cooking spray
- favorite fish seasoning
- optional oregano sprigs

DIRECTIONS · 8 SERVINGS

1. In a large skillet lightly spray with cooking spray and heat over a medium heat.
2. Add garlic and brown.
3. Add onions, peppers, celery, and oregano, cover and cook 10 minutes until vegetables begin to soften, stirring often.
4. Add tomatoes and vinegar, reduce heat cover and cook about 25 minutes.
5. Spray olive oil in 13x9x2 inch glass baking dish. Arrange fish in dish and sprinkle fish with lemon pepper seasoning or favorite fish seasoning, pour tomato mixture over the top.
6. Bake uncovered in 375° oven until fish is just opaque in center about 30-35 minutes (garnish with fresh oregano).

FOODMOVER WINDOWS TO CLOSE PER SERVING

NUTRITION INFORMATION PER SERVING	
CALORIES	144
PROTEIN	22.4g
CARBOHYDRATE	7.4g
TOTAL FAT	2.4g
SODIUM	215mg

SEAFOOD SHOW BOAT

BY JENNIFER BROSS

Tip: All we are saying is give scallops a chance. Richard's secret for chopping spinach: wash thoroughly to make sure you get out grit (it is always there). Stack spinach and slice like fettucini. Havarti cheese is a variation of Tilsit cheese; it is extremely mild with an open texture and mild flavor. As the cheese ages the flavor may become more pungent. Any mild flavored cheese of your choice may be substituted if Havarti is not available. Can also be prepared by stuffing in hollowed vegetable like a zucchini.

INGREDIENTS

1	zucchini (approximately a pound) sliced
1/4	pound uncooked cleaned shrimp medium size
1/4	pound sea scallops
3	chopped mushrooms
1/2	cup chopped onions
1/2	cup chopped, thawed, and drained spinach
2	finely chopped garlic cloves
2	oz danish Havarti reduced fat cheese
1	tsp ground tarragon
1/2	tsp salt
1/2	tsp black pepper
1-1/3	cups cooked basmati rice
	non stick cooking spray

DIRECTIONS 2 SERVINGS

1. Add cooking spray to a large skillet. Sauté garlic and onions till translucent; add zucchini mushrooms seasonings and sauté about 2 minutes. Add a few teaspoons of water if mixture starts to dry out.
2. Add spinach, shrimp, and scallops and cook for minutes more, stirring constantly. Turn off heat and add cheese. Mix thoroughly.
3. Serve with Basmati rice.

FOODMOVER WINDOWS TO CLOSE PER SERVING

NUTRITION INFORMATION PER SERVING	
CALORIES	276
PROTEIN	35g
CARBOHYDRATE	17g
TOTAL FAT	9g
SODIUM	1120mg

SOME ENCHANTED FLOUNDER

BY NANCY GILLINGHAM

INGREDIENTS

- 4 fl oz wine
- 4 oz flounder, raw
- 1/4 onion, sliced thin to make rings
- 4 tbsp grated Parmesan cheese
- 1 tsp garlic powder
- 3 tbsp bread crumbs
- 1 tsp lemon zest
- 2 tbsp chopped parsley
- 1 pinch salt
- 1/2 tsp pepper
- water

DIRECTIONS 1 SERVING

1. Preheat oven to 325°.
2. Season fish with salt and pepper.
3. Pour wine in glass baking dish and add enough water to cover bottom, 1/8 inch deep.
4. Add fish fillets and cover with onions.
5. Sprinkle fish with Parmesan cheese, garlic powder, lemon zest and bread crumbs.
6. Bake for 15 minutes, uncovered in a 325° F oven until fish flakes.
7. Garnish with a slice of lemon and a sprig of parsley.

Tip: Other types of lean white fish can be used like orange roughy. Most of the alcohol cooks off during cooking.

FOODMOVER WINDOWS TO CLOSE PER SERVING

NUTRITION INFORMATION PER SERVING	
CALORIES	414
PROTEIN	41g
CARBOHYDRATE	24g
TOTAL FAT	9g
SODIUM	700mg

STANDING OVATION SHRIMP SCAMPI

BY RHONDA ERACLEO

Tip: To butterfly shrimp lay backside down and run a sharp knife the long way on the shrimp without cutting all the way to the other side.

INGREDIENTS

2	tbsp garlic
1	14.5 oz can fat free, reduced sodium chicken broth
1	cup chopped mushrooms
4	plum tomatoes
4	oz medium shelled shrimp (butterflied)
1	cup cooked spaghetti
4	tbsp grated Parmesan cheese
2	tbsp chopped parsley
1/2	cup chopped onion

juice of 1 lemon
Pam olive oil cooking spray

DIRECTIONS 2 SERVINGS

1. In skillet sprayed with Pam on medium-high heat; add minced garlic, minced onion and lightly brown.
2. Pour in chicken broth and mushrooms and cook for about 10 minutes.
3. Add in chopped plum tomatoes, lemon and cook for another 5 minutes.
4. Add in shrimp and bring to a boil. Once boiling, turn heat to low and simmer until shrimp is cooked approximately 5 minutes.
5. Serve in bowl over 1/2 cup cooked pasta and sprinkle with 2 tablespoons of Parmesan cheese and parsley.

FOODMOVER WINDOWS TO CLOSE PER SERVING

NUTRITION INFORMATION PER SERVING	
CALORIES	273
PROTEIN	23.3g
CARBOHYDRATE	32.5g
TOTAL FAT	5.7g
SODIUM	342mg

PLAYBILL PORTABELLA PASTA
BY JAY JENSEN

"I've lost 23 lbs already. I am really enjoying converting my old recipes into ones that fit into my new eating lifestyle. In many cases, they actually taste better."

TWO SINGULAR SENSATIONS/VEGGIE PIZZA
BY ANDREA BECK

"The FoodMover has changed my life forever! For the better. I met Tammy, my dear friend through this program. We have become the best of friends and continue to support each other daily with our weight maintenance. We both find that not only the FoodMover but also the videos and website continue to motivate us daily. Having the support of another FoodMover friend is so very valuable to my continued success. 58 lbs in 14 months."

PLAYBILL PORTABELLA PASTA

BY JAY JENSEN

Tip: The first time I tried Portabella mushrooms was in 1968, in Florence, Italy. This little Italian restaurant made these mushrooms that tasted like steak! Well, believe me, this is the healthiest steak you've ever tasted.

INGREDIENTS

- 1 cup chopped onion
- 4 whole portabella mushrooms (sliced)
- 1 chopped green pepper
- 1 chopped red pepper
- 6 minced garlic cloves
- 1/4 cup chopped parsley
- 1 tsp oregano
- 1/2 tsp pepper
- 8 oz red and yellow (if you can get them) cherry tomatoes cut into 1/2
- 4 oz tomato sauce
- 4 cups cooked pasta (fettuccini noodles)
- 2 tbsp sliced basil
- Pam olive oil spray
- pinch salt

DIRECTIONS — 4 (1 CUP PASTA WITH 1 CUP SAUCE) SERVINGS

1. Spray a large skillet with non-fat cooking spray and lightly sauté whole mushrooms, remove and keep warm.
2. Sauté garlic, onions, peppers, herbs and spices.
3. Add 4 oz tomato sauce, simmer for 15 minutes.
4. Serve 1 cup of pasta with 1 portabella mushroom and top with sauce mixture.
5. Garnish with sliced basil.

FOODMOVER WINDOWS TO CLOSE PER SERVING

NUTRITION INFORMATION PER SERVING

CALORIES	287
PROTEIN	11g
CARBOHYDRATE	53g
TOTAL FAT	2g
SODIUM	896mg

SATURDAY NIGHT TOFU

BY ALISON MORRIS

INGREDIENTS

- 1 cup vegetable broth
- 1/2 cup cubed extra firm tofu
- 1 cup chopped broccoli
- 1/2 cup sliced carrot
- 1/2 cup sliced celery
- 1/2 cup chopped green onion
- 1 cup chopped green pepper
- 1/2 cup snow peas
- 1/3 cup low sodium teriyaki sauce
- 2 tbsp garlic powder
- 1 tsp dried red pepper flakes
- 1/2 cup cooked noodles (egg noodles, spaghetti noodles or other pasta of your choice)

DIRECTIONS 1 (3 CUPS, COOKED) SERVING

1. Heat the vegetable broth in a wok or electric skillet.
2. Add in the tofu.
3. Add the vegetables.
4. While the veggies are cooking, add the teriyaki sauce, garlic powder, and red pepper flakes.
5. Keep stirring.
6. Add the cooked noodles.
7. Stir until the veggies are softened and most of the liquid is absorbed.

> *Tip:* Three main types of tofu are available in American grocery stores. Firm tofu is dense and solid and holds up well in stir fry dishes, soups, or the grill. Soft tofu is a good choice for recipes that call for blended tofu or in Oriental soups. Silken tofu is made into a creamy or custard like consistency and is great in blended dishes.

FOODMOVER WINDOWS TO CLOSE PER SERVING

NUTRITION INFORMATION PER SERVING	
CALORIES	497
PROTEIN	27g
CARBOHYDRATE	90g
TOTAL FAT	5.4g
SODIUM	2021mg

TWO SINGULAR SENSATIONS/VEGGIE PIZZA

BY ANDREA BECK

Tip: Prepared crusts are available in most supermarkets; if you like you can even make your own crust. Just choose a recipe that calls for very little fat. Colby cheese is a delicious light flavored cheese. For this pizza you can use any favorite cheese if colby is unavailable.

INGREDIENTS

- 1 12" prepared pizza crust
- 4 small garlic cloves, freshly pressed
- 1 tsp Italian seasoning
- 1 small red onion, sliced
- 1 small red bell pepper, sliced
- 1 small zucchini, sliced
- 1 cup fresh mushrooms, sliced
- 2 tbsp freshly grated Parmesan cheese
- 1/2 cup shredded Colby-jack cheese
- non-stick cooking spray

DIRECTIONS 8 (1/8 OF PIZZA) SERVINGS

1. Place the pizza crust on a pizza pan.
2. Sprinkle the crust with the Colby-jack cheese.
3. Spray the skillet with non-fat cooking spray.
4. Heat and sauté the vegetables, garlic, and Italian seasoning for three minutes. Do not overcook them.
5. Pour the vegetable mixture over the pizza crust and top with Parmesan cheese.
6. Bake for 8-10 minutes.
7. Serve immediately.

FOODMOVER WINDOWS TO CLOSE PER SERVING

NUTRITION INFORMATION PER SERVING	
CALORIES	192
PROTEIN	9.3g
CARBOHYDRATE	28.2g
TOTAL FAT	5.5g
SODIUM	365mg

BRING THE HOUSE UPSIDE DOWN CAKE
BY JEANNETTE SCHWALM

" The FoodMover has helped me to follow a healthy and balanced way of eating. I know I can rely on this program to keep me on track. I find it easy to use and very convenient."

MID-RASPBERRY NIGHT DREAM
BY GALE QUINN

"I have always been in excellent health and worked out on a regular basis. But after my second child, I was finding it hard to lose the extra thirty pounds that I had gained. I have had the problem of not knowing what portions I should eat and what category each food belongs in. Not anymore on the FoodMover program"

BRING THE HOUSE UPSIDE DOWN CAKE

BY JULIE LUCHTEFELD

Tip: This tastes like pineapple upside-down cake. It is best chilled. Ever wonder where poppy seeds come from? Poppy seeds are an ancient spice. The seed capsules were found in Switzerland in prehistoric lake dwellings.

INGREDIENTS

- 20 oz can of crushed pineapple (in its own juices)
- 1 box (1 pound) angel food cake mix
- 1 tbsp poppy seeds
- non-stick cooking spray

DIRECTIONS 12 (1/12 OF CAKE: 2X4 INCH PIECE) SERVINGS

1. Preheat oven to 350°.
2. Fold the pineapple and cake mix together in a mixing bowl, including the juice from the pineapple.
3. Spray a 9x13 inch pan with non-stick cooking spray.
4. Pour the mixture into the pan and top with poppy seeds.
5. Bake for 30 minutes.
6. Optional, garnish with raspberries and pineapple.

FOODMOVER WINDOWS TO CLOSE PER SERVING

NUTRITION INFORMATION PER SERVING	
CALORIES	167
PROTEIN	3g
CARBOHYDRATE	39g
TOTAL FAT	0g
SODIUM	324mg

CHIP ON A HOT TIN ROOF

BY DENISE VIVALDO

INGREDIENTS

- 1-1/3 cup all purpose flour
- 1 tsp baking powder
- 1/2 tsp baking soda
- 1/2 tsp ground allspice
- 3 ripe bananas mashed
- 1 tbsp butter
- 3 tbsp applesauce
- 2/3 cup brown sugar
- 1/2 cup egg substitute
- 1/2 cup chocolate chips (yes I am human)
- pinch salt
- cooking spray

DIRECTIONS 12 (ABOUT 1"EACH) SERVINGS

1. Preheat oven 350°.
2. Coat non stick 8"x4" loaf pan with cooking spray.
3. Mix dry ingredients.
4. In separate bowl mix banana, butter, applesauce, and brown sugar. Beat with an electric hand mixer. Add egg substitute and mix 1 minute.
5. Add dry ingredients and blend together.
6. Fold in chocolate chips.
7. Pour into loaf pan and bake 50 to 60 minutes until toothpick comes out clean.
8. Cool 10-15 min on baking rack.

Tip: Wondering about allspice? Allspice is a single spice whose flavor is similar to a nutmeg blend. It is from the fruit of an evergreen tree found in the Western Hemisphere.

FOODMOVER WINDOWS TO CLOSE PER SERVING

NUTRITION INFORMATION PER SERVING	
CALORIES	167
PROTEIN	3.2g
CARBOHYDRATE	32g
TOTAL FAT	3g
SODIUM	265mg

CHORUS LINE CHOCOLATE CAKE

BY JEANETTE SCHWALM

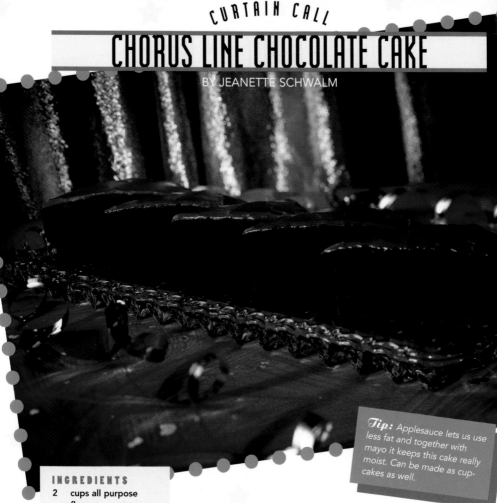

Tip: Applesauce lets us use less fat and together with mayo it keeps this cake really moist. Can be made as cupcakes as well.

INGREDIENTS

- 2 cups all purpose flour
- 3/4 cup white granulated sugar
- 1/2 cup unsweetened cocoa powder
- 1/2 cup apple sauce
- 2 tsp baking soda
- 1 cup low fat mayonnaise
- 1 cup hot water
- 1 tsp vanilla extract
- 2/3 cup powdered sugar
- 2 tbsp unsweetened cocoa powder
- 1/2 tsp vanilla extract
- 2 4 tsp hot water

DIRECTIONS 12 SERVINGS

1. Sift dry ingredients and add wet ingredients (except last four ingredients).
2. Mix well and pour into sprayed non-stick pan 9x13, into two 8" cake pans, or in muffin tins lined with paper cupcakes.
3. Bake for 25-30 minutes, 20 minutes for cupcakes, at 350° or until toothpick comes out clean.
4. Mix icing sugar, cocoa powder, vanilla, and hot water together and spread on cooled cake. Top with glaze.

FOODMOVER WINDOWS TO CLOSE PER SERVING

NUTRITION INFORMATION PER SERVING	
CALORIES	196
PROTEIN	3g
CARBOHYDRATE	41g
TOTAL FAT	2g
SODIUM	398mg

MID-RASPBERRY NIGHT DREAM

5TH PRIZE

BY GALE QUINN

INGREDIENTS

- 10 oz fresh raspberries
- 1 cup white granulated sugar
- 2 tbsp dried egg whites
- 6 tbsp water
- 1/2 tsp almond extract
- 1 tbsp lemon juice
- 4 tsp dried egg whites
- 2 tbsp water
- 1 peeled banana
- 2 9 in ready crust graham pie shells
- dash of salt
- fresh raspberries (garnish)
- mint leaves (optional garnish)

DIRECTIONS | 16 SERVINGS

1. Act one: Like dancing ballerinas, gracefully add the first six ingredients in a bowl; whip for a heavenly 15 minutes. The characters will be light and airy.

2. Act two: The second act whips the dry egg whites with water and banana for 15 minutes, preparing to meet its true love.

3. Act three: The final act, the lovely raspberry meets her dreamy fellow, the Crème de la Crème, and they unite by folding gently together, for a beautiful marriage. The two are now one and are poured evenly into the two piecrusts. Place the new creation in the freezer and freeze until firm (at least 4 hours). Garnish with fresh raspberries and mint.

Tip: Egg whites can be found fresh, frozen and dried in most supermarkets and gourmet stores. Fresh or frozen raspberries can be used to garnish this dish.

FOODMOVER WINDOWS TO CLOSE PER SERVING

NUTRITION INFORMATION PER SERVING	
CALORIES	167
PROTEIN	2g
CARBOHYDRATE	29g
TOTAL FAT	5g
SODIUM	237mg

CURTAIN CALL
MY FAIR SORBET

BY DONNA CHILDS

Tip: Lemon extract makes this light and refreshing.

INGREDIENTS

6   cups strawberries, washed and hulled
1/2 cup sugar
1/4 cup fresh lemon juice
2   tbsp lemon extract
garnish with fresh spearmint or grapefruit or pink grapefruit

DIRECTIONS 8 SERVINGS

1. In a food processor or blender, puree 6 cups of strawberries, washed and hulled.
2. Add sugar, fresh lemon juice, and strawberry liqueur.
3. Pour the mixture into a glass baking dish and freeze, covered for at least 2 hours.
4. Prior to serving, soften the mixture in the refrigerator for 20 minutes and serve in pretty glasses, garnished with mint sprigs.

FOODMOVER WINDOWS TO CLOSE PER SERVING

NUTRITION INFORMATION PER SERVING	
CALORIES	87
PROTEIN	.7g
CARBOHYDRATE	21g
TOTAL FAT	0g
SODIUM	2mg